Challenger Phonics Fun!®

Volume 3 Irregular Vowel Families

Activity and Reading Book

USING the VOLUME 3 ACTIVITY BOOK

TO THE PARENT

"Tips for the Parent" pages are located in the activity book where major skills and concepts are introduced.

The parent will need to determine how much help to give your child. Some students will need constant, detailed guidance, while others may be able to work quickly through the activity book with little assistance.

Before beginning the activity book, both parent and child should become familiar with the video and the songs within the video. Words to the songs are found in this book.

Establish correct reading patterns. Bad habits are sometimes difficult to reverse. Starting in the upper left-hand corner of the page, point to the words and continue from left to right. While reading to the child, call attention to the pertinent *Challenger Phonics Fun* reading skills and concepts.

Remember to praise your child's efforts, to encourage independent thinking, and to have fun! The true joy of learning and ultimately self worth are derived through personal achievement.

Before starting the *Volume 3 Activity and Reading Book*, the student should demon-strate competency with the following skills:

1. Letters and Sounds (Volume 1)

2. Blending (Volumes 1 & 2)

3. One- and Two-Vowel Rules and the Reading Clues (Volume 2)

If the student is not comfortable with these concepts, return to the prior volumes and practice until the student is fluent.

CONCEPTS and SKILLS in VOLUME 3

- **Review Volume 1 Skills**
  Letters and Sounds, Beginning Sounds, and Blending
- **Review Volume 2 Skills**
  One- and Two-Vowel Rules, Digraphs, Plurals, Sight Words, and the Reading Clues
- **Irregular Vowel Families**
- **Consonant Blends**
- **Vowel at the End Rule**
- **C and G Rule**
- **Y at the End Rule**
- **Contractions**
- **Reading**

PRACTICE CARDS
- **Deck 5, One-Vowel Words**
- **Deck 6, Two-Vowel Words**
- **Deck 7, Consonant Blends, Digraphs, and Silent Letters**
- **Deck 8, Irregular Vowel Families**
- **Deck 9, Irregular Vowel Family Words**
- **Deck 10, Sight Words, Soft C and G,**
- **Contractions, Vowel-at-the-End, and**
- **Y-at-the-End Words**

Volume 3 Reading Skills Progress

Have the child complete this survey of phonetic reading skills. Complete the survey periodically, keeping track of the child's progress. Tabulate and record the results at the bottom of the page.

Consonant Blends
Blend each of the following. (1 point each = 10 total points)

bl	cr	fl	gr	sk
scr	sn	spr	str	sw

Irregular-Vowel Families
Read each of the following irregular-vowel families. (1 point each = 32 total points)

	eigh	alk	or	ir
igh	old	au	sion	ind
alt	2 sounds oo	ou	tion	all
ur	3 sounds ed	ay	ing	ew
2 sounds ow	oi	ous	ost	er
ar	oy	ild	aw	

Volume 3 Reading Skills Progress

Irregular Vowel Family Words
Read each of the following irregular-vowel words. (1 point each = 25 total points)

brown	boil	played	mouth	walk
small	mission	car	flew	child
corn	crawl	station	jerk	sleigh
tooth	find	halted	book	fault
toy	hold	slurped	slow	high

Contractions
Read each of the following words. (1 point each = 3 total points)

we're	can't	won't

Soft C & G Words
Read each of the following words. (1 point each = 3 total points)

city	giant	mice

Vowel at the End Words
Read each of the following words. (1 point each = 3 total points)

hi	she	hello

Y at the End Words
Read each of the following words. (1 point each = 3 total points)

baby	try	merry

My Progress
(79 possible)

Date:					
Score:					

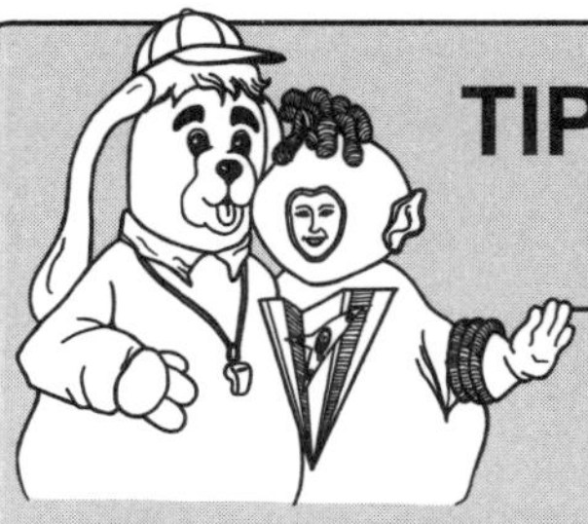

TIPS FOR THE PARENT

The following are instructions and a sample review page. Dialogue is provided, but we encourage you to use your own words, praise, and humor.

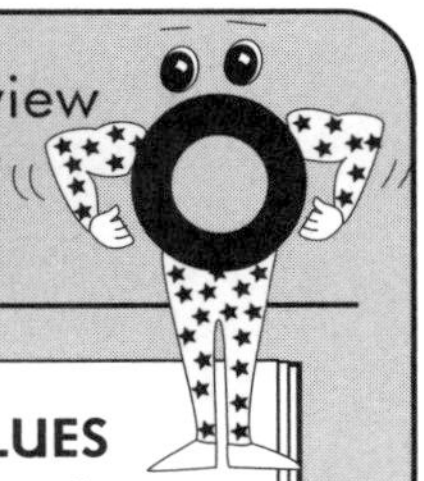

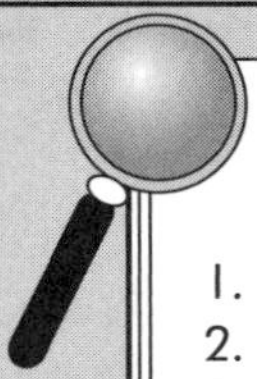

READING CLUES
Look for the vowels.

1. How many vowels?
2. What are the vowels?
3. What will the vowels say?

Read the word.

MARKING THE LONG VOWELS

The vowels are called Power Letters because they can say two sounds—long and short.

When a vowel says its long sound, we put a macron (¯) above it. We cross out the second vowel because it says nothing.

cōat (with the a crossed out)

MARKING THE SHORT VOWELS

When a vowel says its short sound, we put a breve (˘) above it.

căt

READING CLUES

The Reading Clues help determine whether the vowels are long, short, or silent in words or syllables.

Review

1 "Look at the first word. How many vowels? (Two!) Great! So what is the first vowel? (Letter **i**.) What will it say? (Its name!) Yes! What will the second vowel do? (Go to sleep!) You are so smart! Let's read the word. **Kite!** Good!"

"Let's draw a line from the kite to the word, **kite**."

2 "Let's look at the other word. How many vowels does it have? One! Very good. What is the vowel? You are correct - **i**! When letter **i** is the only vowel, what will it say? The short sound! Now, let's read the word. **kiiiit!** Great! Draw a line from the kit to the word, **kit**. Excellent!"

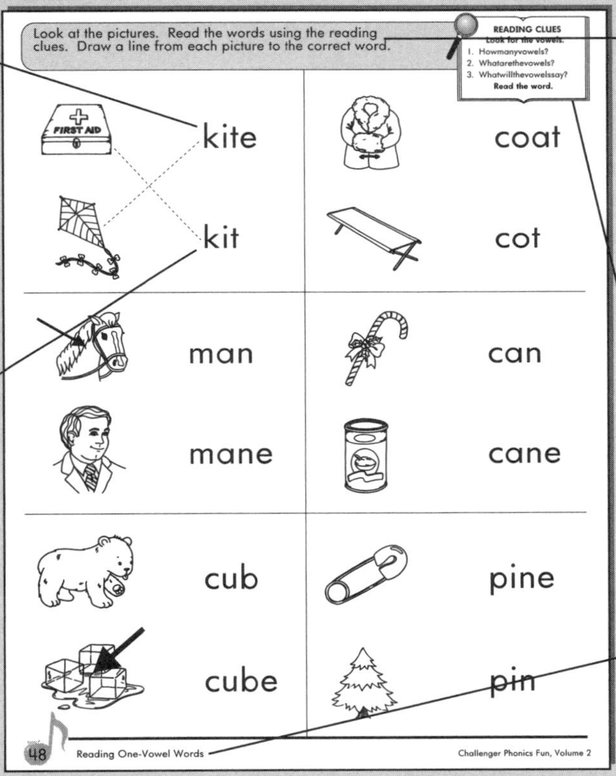

Look at the pictures. Read the words using the reading clues. Draw a line from each picture to the correct word.

READING CLUES
Look for the vowels.
1. Howmanyvowels?
2. Whatarethevowels?
3. Whatwillthevowelssay?
Read the word.

kite
kit
coat
cot
man
mane
can
cane
cub
cube
pine
pin

48 Reading One-Vowel Words
Challenger Phonics Fun, Volume 2

Instructions for the page are written in the shaded box at the top. It is best to read the instructions silently and then instruct the child.

Extra tips may be found in the upper right-hand corners. The parent and the student should both be familiar with the information found here.

This is the skill for this page. Further instructions are in the Parent Guide.

PRACTICE CARDS

For The Concept:	Practice With:
One-Vowel Words	Decks 3 and 5
Two-Vowel Words	Decks 4 and 6
Sight Words, Plurals, Digraphs	Decks 2, 7, 10
One- and Two-Vowel Reading	Readers

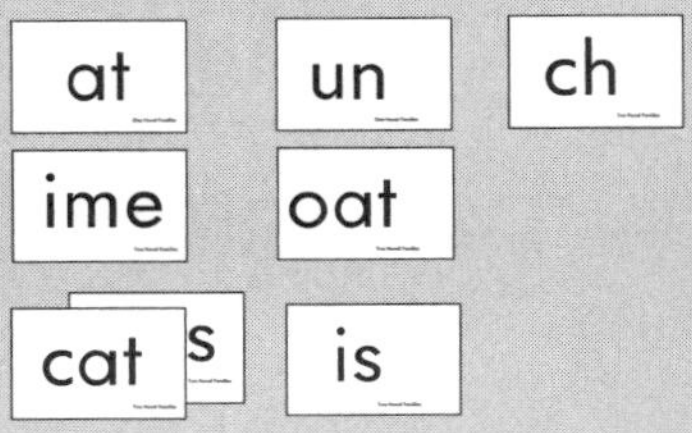
at
un
ch
ime
oat
cat
s
is

Miss Becky and Bitsy

♪ Dear Mr. Martian ♪

Dear Mr. Martian,
I'm writing this to you.
I hope that you will
  write me back
And tell me what you do,
Up there in Mars.

Now, so you'll find my home,
I'll send you my address.
I'll put it on the envelope.
Professor said that would be best.

** I live in a house, on a street,
In a neighborhood,
In a city, in a county, in a state;
In a country, on a continent.
But you need to know more, wait.

My city is _____ .

My county is _____ .

My state is called _____ .

If you were an earthling,

That's all you'd need to know.

But because you're a Martian,

You need more information.

So listen 'cause we have

   some more to go.

I live in _____ (country),

A grand and noble country,

On the continent of _____,

On the planet Earth.**

Now, Mr. Martian,

That's all you need to know,

For your letter to find

   its way to me.

Please write me soon,

And tell me lots of news.

I'll be waiting anxiously.

Apple starts with ă.

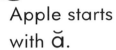

A says "ā and ă."

Bat starts with buh.

B says "buh."

Cat starts with c.

C says "c."

Dog starts with duh.

D says "duh."

Elephant starts with ĕ.

E says "ē and ĕ."

Fish starts with fff.

F says "fff."

These are the upper and lower case letters of the alphabet. Say the names of the pictures. Say the **beginning sound**. Say the letters and their sounds.

Gate starts with g_{uh}.

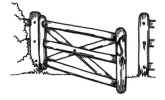

G g

G says "g_{uh}."

Hat starts with h.

H h

H says "h."

Igloo starts with ĭ.

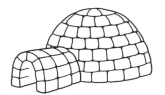

I i

I says "ī and ĭ."

Jack starts with j_{uh}.

J j

J says "j_{uh}."

Kite starts with k.

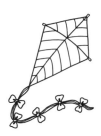

K k

K says "k."

Ladybug starts with lll.

L l

L says "lll."

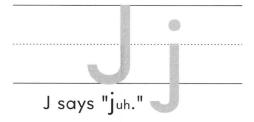

Monkey starts with **mmm**.

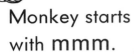

M says "**mmm**."

Net starts with **nnn**.

N says "**nnn**."

Octopus starts with **ŏ**.

O says "**ō** and **ŏ**."

Pan starts with **p**.

P says "**p**."

Queen starts with **q**uh.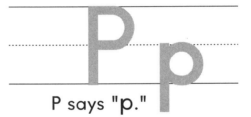

Q says "**q**uh."

Rocket starts with **r**uh.

R says "**r**uh."

These are the upper and lower case letters of the alphabet. Say the names of the pictures. Say the **beginning sound**. Say the letters and their sounds.

Snake starts with **sss**.

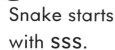

S says "**sss**."

Telephone starts with **t**.

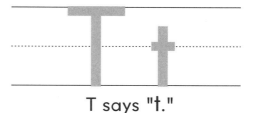

T says "**t**."

Umbrella starts with **ŭ**.

U says "**ū** and **ŭ**."

Vest starts with **vvv**.

V says "**vvv**."

Wagon starts with **W**uh.

W says "**W**uh."

Fox ends with **ks**.

X says "**ks**."

Alphabet, Lower and Uppercase

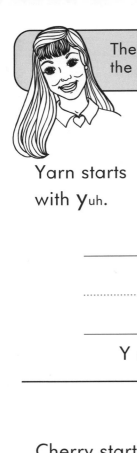

These are the upper and lower case letters of the alphabet. Say the names of the pictures. Say the **beginning sound**. Say the letters and their sounds.

Yarn starts with y_{uh}.

Y says "y_{uh}."

Zipper starts with zzz.

Z says "zzz."

Cherry starts with ch.

Ch says "ch."

Ship starts with sh.

Sh says "sh."

Whale starts with wh.

Wh says "wh."

Thumb starts with th.

Th says "th."

Say the name of the picture. What is the **beginning** sound? Circle the letter that makes that sound. Trace the letter in the lines.

j   m   (i)

h   n   f

i

h

p   q   d

y   u   a

p

y

n   e   q

k   u   n

q

u

igloo • pig • quail

house • yawn • umbrella

Beginning Letters and Sounds

13

Say the name of the picture. What is the **beginning** sound? Circle the letter that makes that sound. Trace the letter in the lines.

y   c   o

_____
o

v   h   r

_____
v

i   e   w

_____
e

z   a   f

_____
a

d   k   e

_____
k

b   r   p

_____
b

ostrich • elephant • kite

volcano • apple • bell

Say the name of the picture. What is the **beginning** sound? Circle the letter that makes that sound. Trace the letter in the lines.

w   c   p   e   l   c

_____
w

_____
c

n   g   y   t   r   n

_____
y

_____
r

b   q   j   b   l   m

_____
j

_____
m

web • yawn • jet   cow • rabbit • moose

Say the name of the picture. What is the **beginning** sound? Circle the letter that makes that sound. Trace the letter in the lines.

f   j   k   th   l   t

f   th

sh   th   ch   s   sh   ch

ch   sh

ph   wh   sh   z   s   i

wh   z

fox • chair • whale   thimble • shirt • zig-zag

Say the name of the picture. What is the **ending** sound? Circle the letter that makes that sound. Trace the letter in the lines.

cot • fox • doll

octopus • wagon • tag

Ending Letters and Sounds

17

Say the name of the picture. What is the **ending** sound? Circle the letter that makes that sound. Trace the letter in the lines.

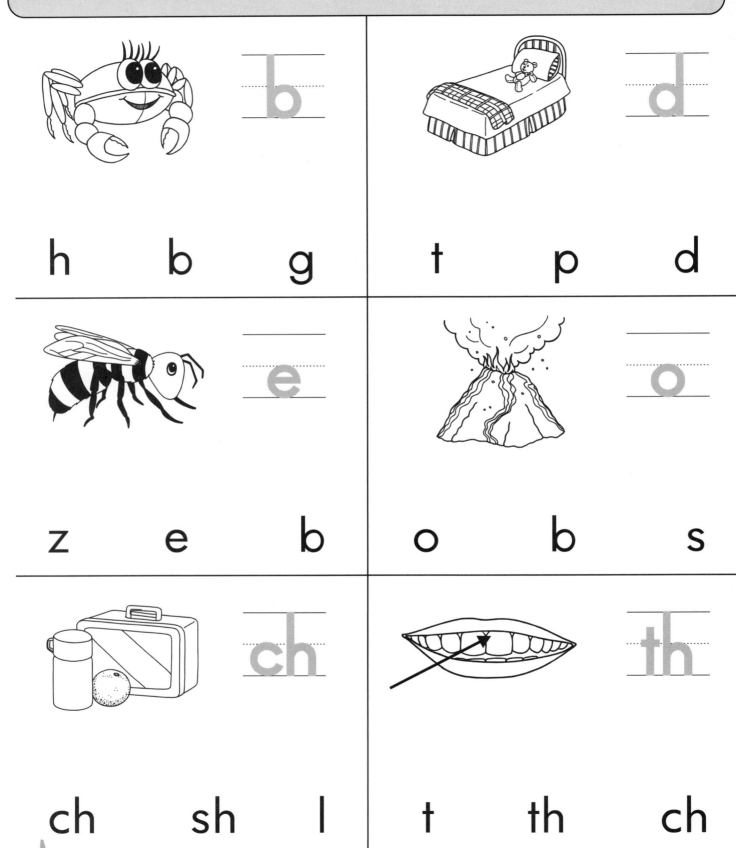

h   b   g   t   p   d

z   e   b   o   b   s

ch   sh   l   t   th   ch

crab • bee • lunch   bed • volcano • teeth

Say the name of the picture. What is the **beginning** sound? Circle the letter that makes that sound. Trace the letter in the lines.

 ch

 sh

 wh

 th

 ph

---

ch

(sh)

wh

th

ph

ch

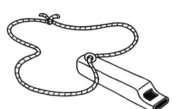

sh

th

ch

sh

th

sh

ship • phone • chimney

whistle • thorn • shirt

Digraphs

Put your magic finger on the **u** and say the short sound (ŭ). Keep your motor running as you move your finger toward the **m**. When your finger reaches the **m**, say "**mmm**" until you take your finger off. Find your **Letters and Sounds Cards** and repeat the activity.

"What does the **u** say? Right! **uuuu** (ŭ)"

u

"What does the **m** say? Right! **mmmm**."

m

"Now let's put them closer together! **uuummm**!" (Use short ŭ.)

u   m

"Now let's put them next to each other
and say them quickly!
"**um**" as in
"**Hum** with me!"

um

Hum with me!

Blend the word. Draw a line from the word to the correct picture. Write the correct word next to the picture.

dog

cat

pen

bun

kit

cat

dog

bun

pen

kit

What makes the vowels special? They make two sounds! Say the two sounds (long and short) of each vowel.

The Five Power Letters

eel

ape

apple

eggs

ice

in

old

octopus

unicycle

umbrella

Circle the five vowels.

a b c d e f g h i j k l m
n o p q r s t u v w x y z

Write the five vowels.

Write four consonants.

♪ Challenger One-Vowel Song ♪

When there's one vowel
in a word or syllable,
the vowel is usually short!

(Repeat)

Sing the **Challenger One-Vowel Song.** Look at the picture. Read the words. Mark the vowels with breves. Circle the word that describes the picture.

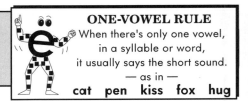
   (hŭt)   hŏt   nŏt

   jam   jack   Pat

   pen   ten   pan

   rat   red   hat

   rot   rod   hop

hut • jam • pan • hat • rod

Circle the one-vowel family that is in the name of the picture.

(at)   op    ob   ub

 an   am    it   in

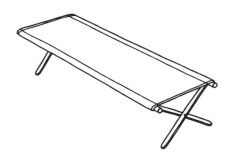 ob   ot    en   ep

rat • man • cot   tub • kit • hen

One-Vowel Families   25

I   the   a   is   no   my   here

My dog is Max.

This is a raft.

I am a frog.

The van is here.

This fish is big.

The jet is big.

I am a dish.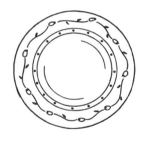

This dog sits.

♪ Challenger Two-Vowel Song ♪

 kīt∉

bē∉

mūl∉

chā∕n

bō∅t

When two vowels go walking,
The first one does the talking.
It makes a sound just like its name.
The second one goes to sleep.

(Repeat)

Good-night!

Read each word. Mark the first vowel with a macron. Cross out the sleeping vowel. Draw a line from the word to the correct picture. Write the word in the lines.

k͞ite

tree

ch͞ain

cake

bee

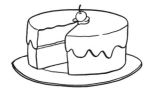

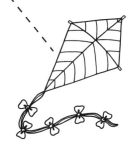

chain

cake

kite

bee

tree

Read each word. Mark the first vowel with a macron. Cross out the sleeping vowel. Draw a line from the word to the correct picture. Write the word in the lines.

hīve

road

cāpe

bīke

tube

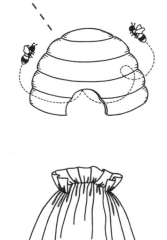

hive

Sing the **Challenger Two-Vowel Song**. Look at the picture. Read the words. Mark the first vowels with macrons. Cross out sleeping vowels. Circle the word that describes the picture.

      trāin   kīte

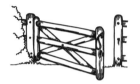   skate   gate   nail

   rain   cane   mane

   feet   leaf   plate

   jeep   cute   mule

bone • gate • cane • leaf • cute

Two-Vowel Words

The Detective found the Reading Clues! Follow the clues to help you read. When we know whether the vowel says its short or long sound, reading is easy!

 READING CLUES
Look for the vowels.
1. How many vowels?
2. What is the vowel?
3. What will the vowel say?
Read the word.

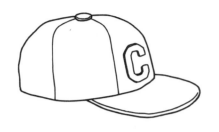

cap

① Circle the number of vowels that are in the word.

 1   2

② What is the vowel?

 a   e

i   o   u

③ What will the vowel say?

ā   ǎ

There is one vowel, so it will say the short sound, ǎ. Circle the correct vowel sound.

④ Read the word:

cap

The Detective found the Reading Clues! Follow the clues to help you read. When we know whether the vowel says its short or long sound, reading is easy!

READING CLUES
Look for the vowels.
1. How many vowels?
2. What are the vowels?
3. What will the vowels say?
Read the word.

cape

---

1 Circle the number of vowels that are in the word.

1   **2**

2 What are the vowels?

a   e

i   o   u

---

3 What will the vowels say?

ā   ă

There are two vowels, so the first, **a**, will say its name - the long sound. The second vowel, **e**, will go to sleep. Circle the correct vowel sound.

4 Read the word:

cape

© 2003 The Learning Crew

Change the one-vowel word to a two-vowel word. Add letter **e** to make **can** say **cane**. Mark the vowels with breves for short vowels or macrons for long vowels. Cross out the sleeping vowels.

READING CLUES
Look for the vowels.
1. How many vowels?
2. What are the vowels?
3. What will the vowels say?
Read the word.

can

cane

bắt

cānẹ́

flag

game

cake

hat

jạm

hand

gate

READING CLUES
Look for the vowels.
1. How many vowels
2. What are the vowels?
3. What will the vowels say?
Read the word.

Change the one-vowel word to a two-vowel word. Add letter **a** to make **bed** say **bead**. Mark the vowels with breves for short vowels or macrons for long vowels. Cross out the sleeping vowels.

bed

bead

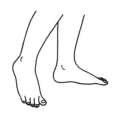

feet

eggs

bee

net

seal

elf

eel

deer

web

Look at the pictures. Read the words using the reading clues.
Draw a line from each picture to the correct word.

READING CLUES
Look for the vowels.
1. How many vowels
2. What are the vowels?
3. What will the vowels say?
Read the word.

kite

kit

coat

cot

man

mane

can

cane

cub

cube

pine

pin

Look at the pictures. Read the words using the reading clues.
Draw a line from each picture to the correct word.

READING CLUES
Look for the vowels.
1. How many vowels
2. What are the vowels?
3. What will the vowels say?
Read the word.

pan

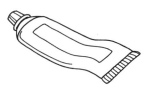

tub

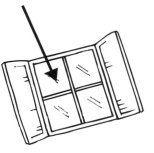

pane

tube

tape

rain

tap

ran

bed

cap

bead

cape

Say the name of the picture. Is it plural or not?
Circle the word that describes the picture.

egg

eggs

tree

trees

dog

dogs

cake

cakes

cat

cats

seal

seals

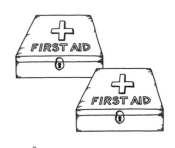

kit

kits

bee

bees

Say the names of the pictures. Read the words. Draw line from each word to the picture it describes.

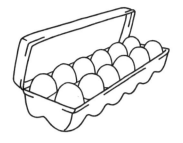

bats

eggs

bugs

cats

kites

coats

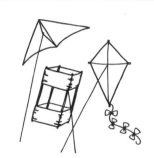

grapes

leaves

cubs

cubes

Plurals

Read the sentence. Circle the correct answer, **yes** or **no**. Put a cirle around the sight words that we have learned.

(Here) (is) Tag, (my) horse.

yes

no

I am Max, the dog.

yes

no

My dog will eat oats.

yes

no

I like my dog and my horse.

yes

no

Here is Gugenheimer.

yes

no

I am Tag, the horse.

yes

no

Here is a mug.

yes

no

This is a fox with kits.

yes

no

This is a mom with a kid.

yes

no

♩ Bric and Brac ♪

Bric and Brac,
green and blue
out for an adventure.

They clippety climb with
Creepy, crawly crab,
And meet a dreadful dragon.

Unafraid, Bric and Brac
Flip and fly to safety.

Frowny frog caught in globby glue--
A very grouchy Grump!
"Bric and Brac,
Please play with me,"
Says Prissy Prickly Prune.

They slip and slide
with Sneezy Snake
and very scary scorpion.

Quiet Queen
with Bric and Brac--
Sparkle and spin
when spring has sprung.

Swiftly swing on a striped string,
As they climb the skinny skyscraper.

Two consonants,
Together, Bric and Brac,
Blending their adventure!

Twisty, twirly, tricky trip--
They streak to a
screechy stop!

Read the words. Say the name of the picture. Circle the word that describes the picture. Underline the consonant blends.

price

(prune)

preen

frog

fruit

freeze

snake

snap

snail

glide

glue

gloss

strike

strong

street

broke

Brac

brake

prune • snake • strong

frog • glue • Brac

Consonant Blend Words

Underline the consonant blends. Read the words. Circle the word that describes the picture. Trace the consonant blend in the lines.

45

Bric   Brad   slow   slide

Br   sl

brim   brush   block   blue

br   bl

slope   sled   flip   flag

sl   fl

Consonant Blend Words   45

Underline the consonant blends. Read the words. Circle the word that describes the picture. Trace the consonant blend in the lines.

crab   (crib)

stuck   stick

cr

st

grapes   grab

twine   twist

gr

tw

slope   sled

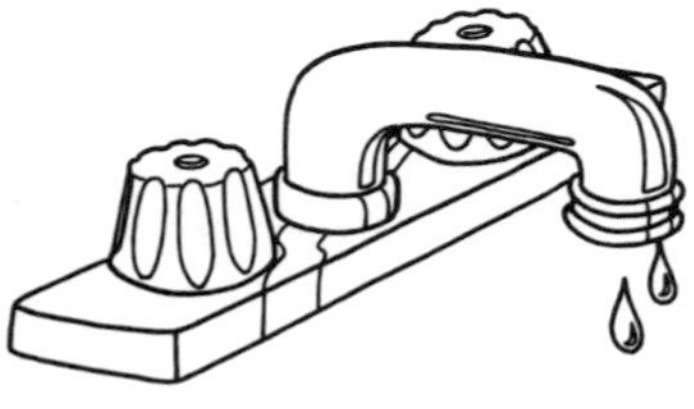

flip   flag

sl

fl

(spoon)   speck   blend   black

sp   bl

sweep   swell   plum   plus

sw   pl

crack   crab   clock   clip

cr   cl

TIPS FOR THE PARENT

IRREGULAR VOWEL FAMILIES

An **irregular vowel family** is a group of letters that do not follow the one- and two-vowel rules.

It is critically important for beginning readers to memorize the irregular vowel families, the same way they learned the alphabet letters.

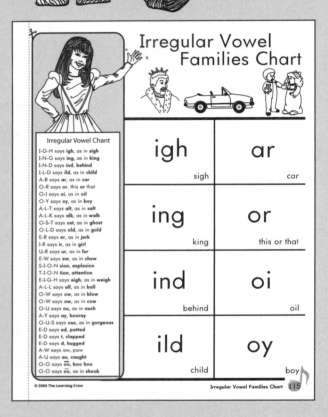

Irregular Vowel Families Chart

Irregular Vowel Chant

I-G-H says **igh**, as in **sigh**
I-N-G says **ing**, as in **king**
I-N-D says **ind**, **behind**
I-L-D says **ild**, as in **child**
A-R says **ar**, as in **car**
O-R says **or**, this **or** that
O-I says **oi**, as in **oil**
O-Y says **oy**, as in **boy**
A-L-T says **alt**, as in **salt**
A-L-K says **alk**, as in **walk**
O-S-T says **ost**, as in **ghost**
O-L-D says **old**, as in **gold**
E-R says **er**, as in **jerk**
I-R says **ir**, as in **girl**
U-R says **ur**, as in **fur**
E-W says **ew**, as in **chew**
S-I-O-N **sion**, explosion
T-I-O-N **tion**, attention
E-I-G-H says **eigh**, as in **weigh**
A-L-L says **all**, as in **ball**
O-W says **ow**, as in **blow**
O-W says **ow**, as in **cow**
O-U says **ou**, as in **ouch**
A-Y says **ay**, hooray
O-U-S says **ous**, as in **gorgeous**
E-D says **ed**, patted
E-D says **t**, clapped
E-D says **d**, hugged
A-W says **aw**, paw
A-U says **au**, caught
O-O says **oo**, boo hoo
O-O says **oo**, as in **shook**

igh	ar
sigh	car
ing	**or**
king	this or that
ind	**oi**
behind	oil
ild	**oy**
child	boy

© 2003 The Learning Crew — Irregular Vowel Families Chart 115

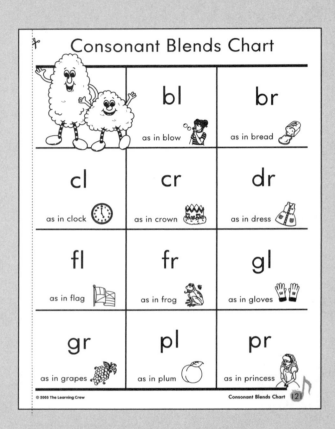

Consonant Blends Chart

bl	br
as in blow	as in bread
cl	**cr**	**dr**
as in clock	as in crown	as in dress
fl	**fr**	**gl**
as in flag	as in frog	as in gloves
gr	**pl**	**pr**
as in grapes	as in plum	as in princess

© 2003 The Learning Crew — Consonant Blends Chart 121

PRACTICE CARDS FOR IRREGULAR VOWEL and CONSONANT BLEND skills:

Irregular Vowel Families
Deck 8

igh

Irregular Vowel Family Words
Deck 9

night

Consonant Blends
Deck 7

st

Make new words with Decks 3, 4, 7

st	ring		r	ake
b	ay		c	ar
sl	ip		br	oke

The sleigh scoots faster than quick motion in the cold snow.

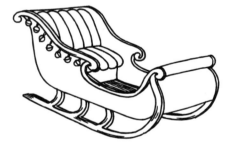

It is a rough ride through the night for Miss Debby.

♪ Irregular Vowel Families Song ♪

IGH		igh	ING		ing
high	light		king	ring	
night	sight		spring	whing-ding	

IND		ind	ILD		ild
find	kind		mild	or	
mind	behind		wild	child	

AR		ar	OR		or
car	far		born	for	
star			corn		

OI		oi	OY		oy
moist	oil		boy	toy	
boil			joy		

ALT	alt	ALK	alk
halt malt		chalk talk	
salt waltz		walk	

OST	ost	OLD	old
most post		cold sold	
almost		gold	

ER	er	IR	ir
her jerk		bird first	
clerk		girl	

UR	ur	EW	ew
purple turkey		few new	
nurse		mew	

mew

Irregular Vowel Families Song

SION sion		**TION** tion	
passion		fiction	
mission		auction	**N**
decision		direction	

EIGH eigh	**8**	**ALL** all	
freight		tall mall	
weight		ball wall	
eight		fall	

OW ow		**OW** ow	
blow		How now	
low		brown cow?	
slow			

OU ou		**AY** ay	
shout		May	March
out		play	**5**
loud		day	Tuesday

OUS   ous

nervous

famous

gorgeous

ED   says   "ed"

patted

landed

lifted

OST   ost

walked   hopped

skipped   stopped

ED   says   "d"

played   chewed

cried   hugged

AW   aw

hawk

saw

paw

AU   au

taught

fault

haul

OO   oo

zoo

boo

hoo

OO   oo

look at a book

Irregular vowels, exceptions to the rules. "Aren't they jewels?" Irregular vowels.

eigh

Miss Debby has
a sleigh.

Find and circle the **eight sleighs.**

Look at the picture. Read the words. Circle the word that describes the picture. Write that word in the lines. Read the portion of the sleigh story at the bottom of the page.

8

(eight)   neigh   _eight_

sleigh   weigh

neighbor   eight   _____

freight   sleigh

sleigh   weigh   _____

neighbor   eight

neigh   freight   _____

eight   sleigh

eight • sleigh • weigh • neigh

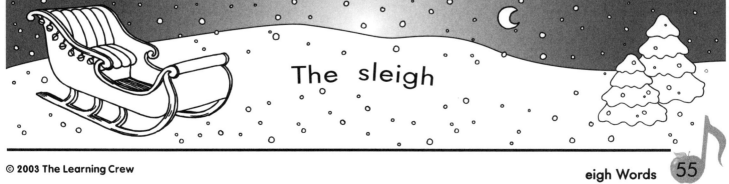

The sleigh

eigh Words   **55**

♪ Hook and Loop ♪

We're H<u>oo</u>k and L<u>oo</u>p,
The double- O Sp<u>oo</u>ks,
We're here to give you the sc<u>oo</u>p.

Double O says "o͞o" and "o͝o"
Two O's together say "o͞o" --
Two O's together say "o͞o."

N<u>oo</u>dle, p<u>oo</u>dle, b<u>oo</u>st and r<u>oo</u>st;
T<u>oo</u>t, b<u>oo</u>t, bl<u>oo</u>m and br<u>oo</u>m.

M<u>oo</u>n, sp<u>oo</u>n,
s<u>oo</u>n, ball<u>oo</u>n.
T<u>oo</u>l, sch<u>oo</u>l,
r<u>oo</u>m and B<u>OO</u>M!

Boo!

Our favorite game is L<u>oo</u>by - L<u>oo</u>;
Our favorite word is B<u>OO</u>!

We're H<u>oo</u>k and L<u>oo</u>p,
The double - O sp<u>oo</u>ks,
We're here to give you a l<u>oo</u>k.

Double O says "o͞o" and "o͞o"
Two O's together say "o͞o" --
Two O's together say "o͝o."

C<u>oo</u>kie, r<u>oo</u>kie, br<u>oo</u>k and cr<u>oo</u>k.
H<u>oo</u>k, t<u>oo</u>k, n<u>oo</u>k and c<u>oo</u>k.
R<u>oo</u>k sh<u>oo</u>k, l<u>oo</u>k at a b<u>oo</u>k.

Two O's say "o͝o;"
But most say "o͞o."
It's been a h<u>oo</u>t,
But we must sc<u>oo</u>t.

T<u>oo</u>dle - <u>oo</u>.
B<u>OO</u>!

Hook and Loop Song 57

Two oo's say "o͞o" as in . .

boo hoo

ball oon

The sleigh scoots . . .

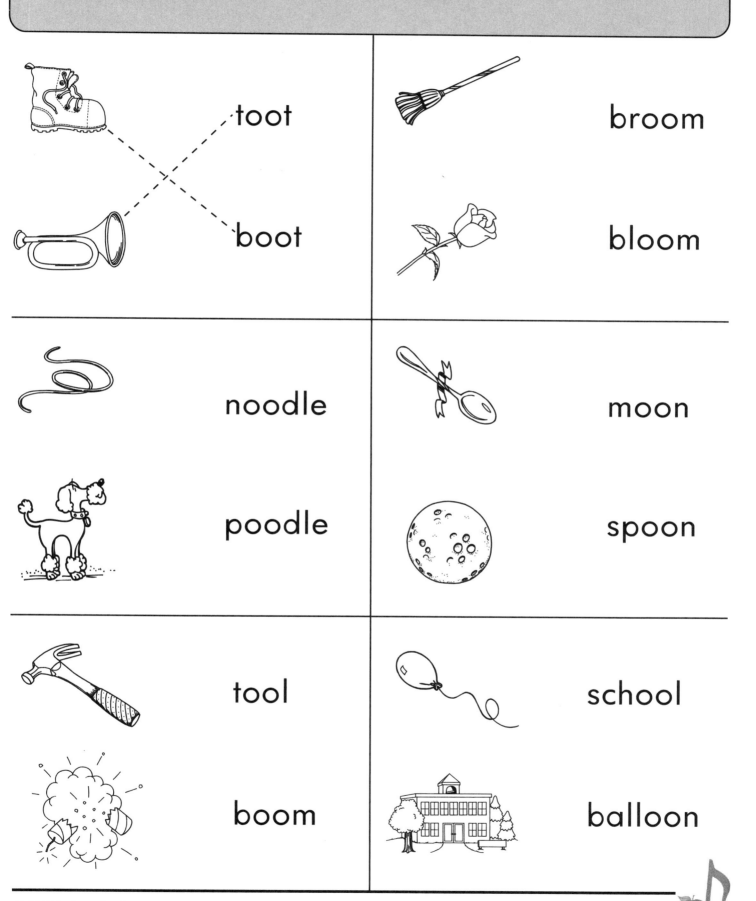

toot

boot

broom

bloom

noodle

poodle

moon

spoon

tool

boom

school

balloon

Two oo's say "ŏŏ" as in . . .

Look at a book.

The sleigh scoots . . .

Look at the picture. Read the words. Circle the word that describes the picture.

(cookie)

brook

crook

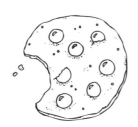

hook

took

cook

shook

look

book

cookie

brook

crook

hook

took

cook

rook

shook

book

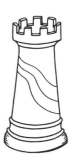

cookie • book • Hook

cook • crook • rook

Double-o Words (short)

Remember the Er Brothers? Read what each of them said to the Professor.

"We're the
Er Brothers!
But we
have no
sisters!"

"Get the
dirt
right out
of the
shirt!"

"Turn
and churn
but don't
let it
burn!"

Look at the picture. Read the words. Circle the word that describes the picture.

mother

 father

fern

tiger

him

her

quarter

brother

father • her

tiger • quarter

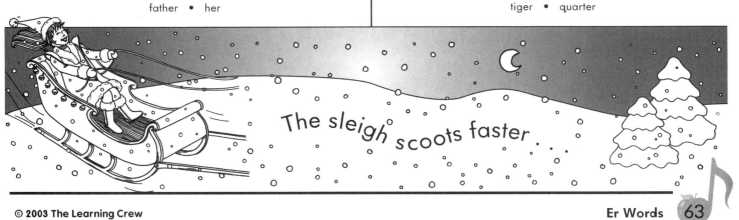

The sleigh scoots faster . . .

Er Words 63

(girl)

sir

grill

twirl

bird

fir

third

swirl

skirt

shirt

stir

skirt

first

fir

mirth

third

whirl

first

1st   2nd   3rd

girl • skirt • fir

bird • shirt • third

Look at the picture. Read the words. Circle the word that describes the picture.

turkey

purple

curl

fur

burn

churn

further

purse

curd

gurgle

burger

nurse

spurn

curve

curb

turtle

turn

hurl

turkey • purse • curve

fur • nurse • turtle

Ur Words

When a C is followed by K,

the C makes a copy-cat sound

just like the K,

and the word ends with the sound k.

The sleigh scoots faster than quick . . .

Look at the picture. Read the words. Circle the word that describes the picture.

quarter

quail

quick

queen

quart

quip

quarters

quarts

quail • quart

queen • quarters

chic

chick

duks

ducks

lock

lok

bloks

block

soc

sock

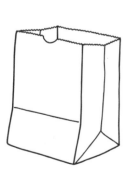

sak

sack

TIPS FOR THE PARENT

Many concepts are taught in Volume 3. Here are some of the rules that we practice in the activity pages.

Miss Debby teaches the vowel rules on the video. The rules appear on pages that cover these concepts, in the top, right-hand corners. Help the student understand the rule before beginning the page.

VOWEL AT THE END RULE

When there's a one-vowel
syllable or word,
and the vowel is on the end,
that vowel is usually long.

C & G RULE

When a C or G is followed
by E, I, or Y, the C says
"**sss**" and the G says "**juh**."

Y AT THE END RULE

When you have a one-syllable word,
and Y comes at the end (there's no other vowel),
The Y says "ī"-

When two or more syllables form a word,
And Y comes at the end,
The Y says "e"!

PRACTICE CARDS FOR THE SKILLS:

Irregular Vowel Families Decks 8 and 9	eigh	ow	string
Consonant Blends Deck 7	fr	sw	
Vowel at the End Deck 10	she	be	
Y at the End Deck 10	why	baby	

♪ So Hello! ♪

When there's a one-vowel
Syllable or word,
And the vowel is on the end,
That vowel is usually long,
Usually long, usually long.

Words like <u>me</u>, <u>he</u>,
<u>She</u>, <u>we</u>, <u>be</u> -
<u>No</u>, <u>go</u>, <u>so</u>,
<u>Hi</u>, <u>ho</u>, hel<u>lo</u>!

<u>Di</u>nosaur, <u>du</u>plicate,
<u>Si</u>ren, <u>fa</u>ble and <u>hi</u>bernate!

Remember this rule,
And you'll never
Go Wrong!
Never
Go Wrong!

Read the sentence using each "vowel at the end" syllable.
Circle the syllable that correctly completes the word.
Can you write that syllable on the line?

VOWEL AT THE END RULE
When there's a one-vowel syllable or word, and the vowel is on the end, that vowel is usually long.

We can read a _____ per.

no   lu   (pa)

A _____ lar bear lives in the snow.

so   po   ro

This is a pair of _____ ers.

pli   tri   sti

Here is a big _____ nosaur.

do   di   du

Can you play with a _____ - _____.

yo   do   ya

Read the sentence using each "vowel at the end" syllable.
Circle the syllable that correctly completes the word.
Can you write that syllable on the line?

VOWEL AT THE END RULE
When there's a one-vowel
syllable or word,
and the vowel is on the end,
that vowel is usually long.

The line is ____ agonal.

di   bi   do

This is a ____ cycle.

to   mo   bi

The balloons are ____ plicates.

bo   di   du

This is a ____ cycle.

pa   bi   tri

This shape is a ____ amond.

du   di   de

Read the sentence. Put a line under the word or syllable that ends with a vowel. Circle the picture that the sentence describes.

A rat is <u>so</u> small.

He has no hair!

He will say hello.

This car can go fast.

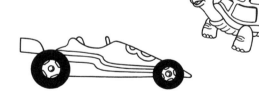

She will eat donuts.

so • He <u>no</u> • He hel<u>lo</u> • go • She donuts

♪ AttenTION! ♪

When I see a "tion"
at the end of a word . . .
T-I-O-N!   S-I-O-N!

Give me those "tion" words,
as in "atten<u>tion</u>"
T-I-O-N!   T-I-O-N!

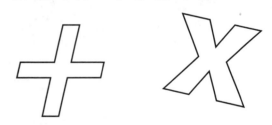

Did I ever men<u>tion</u>
The calcula<u>tion</u> ques<u>tion</u>?
Multiplica<u>tion</u>, addi<u>tion</u>,
   subtrac<u>tion</u>,

For an educa<u>tion</u>,
It takes ac<u>tion</u> and exer<u>tion</u>.

When I see a "sion"
at the end of a word . . .
S-I-O-N!   S-I-O-N!

Give me those "sion" words,
as _in_ "television"
S-I-O-N! S-I-O-N!

Do you want admis<u>sion</u>
To see the colli<u>sion</u>?
Then the explo<u>sion</u> brings
Confu<u>sion</u> and divi<u>sion</u>!

In conclu<u>sion</u>, remember this expres<u>sion</u>,
"Pay them atten<u>tion</u>!"
T-I-O-N!   and
S-I-O-N!

nation

station

(vacation)

mansion

tension

version

lotion

motion

potion

passion

pension

television

action

question

fraction

?

decision

explosion

erosion

vacation • lotion • question

mansion • television • explosion

The sleigh scoots faster than quick motion . . .

Here is the lotion.

 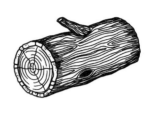

Here is the television.

Here is a collision.

The occasion is a birthday.

Look at the picture. Read the words. Circle the word that describes the picture. Write the word in the lines. Read the portion of the sleigh story at the bottom of the page.

old says "old" as in cold.

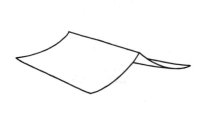

 fold

bold

mold

sold

old

mold

gold

sold

The sleigh scoots faster than quick motion in the cold . . .

Look at the picture. Read the words. Circle the correct word that describes the picture. Read the portion of the sleigh story at the bottom of the page.

OW says "ow" as in snow.

(mow)

low

fast

slow

blow

flow

tow

two

The sleigh scoots faster than quick motion in the cold snow

Ow Words 79

When a C or a G is followed by
E, I, or Y,
the C says "**sss**" and the G says "**j**uh."

Circle the soft C and G words. Color the picture.

Did you see the (gentle) giant race the aged mice?

The C's in these words say **sss**.	The G's in these words say **j**uh.
ice	gem
lace	huge
circus	ginger
city	giraffe

Read the words. Underline the soft C or G with the vowel that follows. Circle the word that describes the picture.

ice

race

city

gym

giraffe

sage

circus

mice

cell

giant

ginger

age

lace

rice

celery

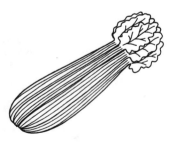

huge

gentle

cage

ice • mice • celery

giraffe • giant • cage

Read each sentence. Draw a line from the sentence to the correct picture. Underline each word that has a soft C or G in it.

The circus tent is big.

Here is the city.

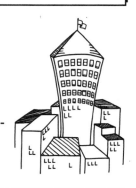

This is a bowl of rice.

The snail's pace is slow.

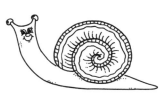

See the shiny gems?

The huge balloon pops.

The cookie is made with ginger.

What age is the baby?

circus city • rice pace • gems huge • age ginger

♪ O-U-G-H ♪

O-U-G-H!

m-m-m . . .

O-U-G-H!

m-m-m . . .

You can say O-U-G-H
in six different ways.

Although, my friend,
we've never fought,
you said you had
the horse I sought;
to meet me in Poughkeepsie
and you'd sell him to me.

I bought the horse that you brought,
because I thought that I ought.
I met you at the trough;
At the price I had to cough.
Although a lot, I paid the dough.

I chased my horse to the sl<u>ough</u>.
I found him up on a tree b<u>ough</u>.
Th<u>ough</u> I'm really t<u>ough</u>,
My horse is just too r<u>ough</u>.
I think, I think I've had en<u>ough</u>.

O-U-G-H!

m-m-m . . .

O-U-G-H!

m-m-m . . .

O-U-G-H!

m-m-m . . .

O-U-G-H!

I'm through!

Read the words. Circle the word that describes the picture. Note that the words sound alike.

muff   tough

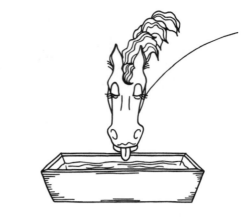

off   trough

hot   fought

oh   dough

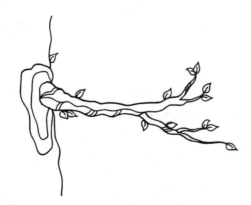

cow   bough

tough • fought • bough

moo   slough

trough • dough • slough

igh says "ī" as in night.

light

right

night

tight

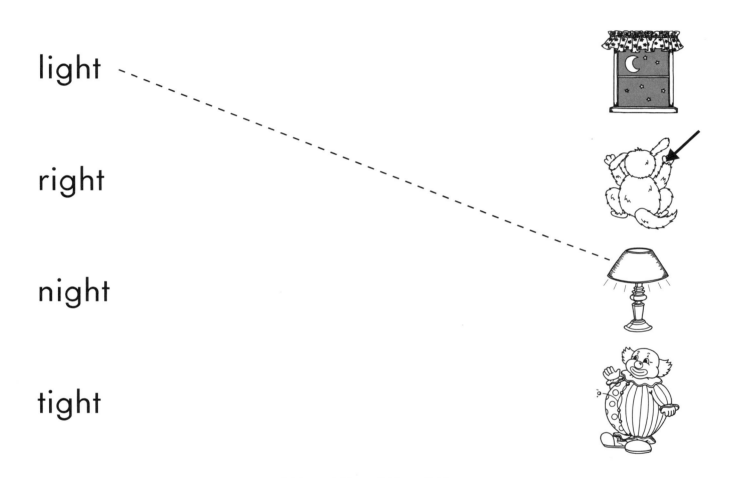

night • right • light • tight

The sleigh scoots faster than quick motion in the cold snow.
It is a rough ride through the night . . .

Igh Words **87**

or says "or" as in **corn.**

---

fork

corn

forty

Cory

forty

Cory • forty • fork • corn

The sleigh scoots faster than quick motion in the cold snow.
It is a rough ride through the night for Miss Debby.

I like ice on a hot day.

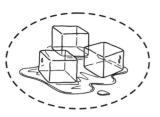 

It is fun to go to the circus.

The giraffe is at the zoo.

The aged mice race the gentle giant.

This is a bird cage.

Here is the gentle giant.

Soft C and G Sentences **89**

♪ Y at the End ♪

When you have
   a one-syllable word,
And Y comes at the end
   (there's no other vowel),

The Y says "ī",
   let's give it a try,
And see what words
   we can blend
   (we can blend).

My - try to fly
   (don't you cry),
A fox is sly, tell me why
   (tell me why).

My - pry and ply
   (that's my guy).
Buy to fry, by and by
   (by and by).

When two or more syllables
form a word,
And Y comes at the end
(at the end),

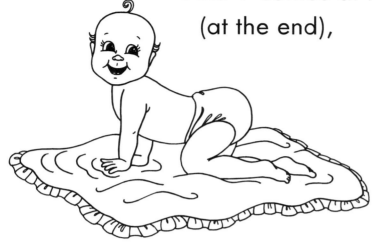

The Y says "ē",
so try it with me,
And see what words
we can blend
(we can blend)

Mommy's and daddy's
tiny, happy baby,
Creepy, crawly,
not weepy or sleepy.

Doggy and kitty
sing a silly ditty,
Merry, jazzy, and a
teeny bit noisy.

Y says "ē" at the end.
That's Y at the end.

Y at the End Song (Y at the End Rules)

Circle the word that describes the picture.

Y AT THE END RULE
When you have a one-syllable word,
and Y comes at the end (there's no other vowel),
The Y says "ī"—

When two or more syllables form a word,
And Y comes at the end,
The Y says "ē"!

why   (Debby)   yarn

story   pony   lady

Marzy   sly   yard

sleepy   try   pony

story   joy   baby

Debby • lady • Marzy • pony • baby

Circle the word that describes the picture.

Y AT THE END RULE
When you have a one-syllable word,
and Y comes at the end (there's no other vowel),
The Y says "ī"–

When two or more syllables form a word,
And Y comes at the end,
The Y says "ē"!

my   cry   merry

cry   fry   try

by   yoke   fly

sky   fry   yo-yo

sty   my   shy

cry • fry • fly • sky • shy

Read each sentence. Circle the contractions.

CONTRACTIONS
A contraction is two words that are short-ened and joined together to make one.

she will - she'll, it is - it's, we are - we're

she will | (She'll) hide near a rock.

I will | I'll sit in the sea.

you will | You'll like our pals.

we will | We'll take a hike.

CONTRACTIONS
A contraction is two words that are short-ened and joined together to make one.

is not - isn't, do not - don't, can not - can't

is not	Cory isn't Letter Lady. 
can not	He can't sit on a bough! 
will not	Gugy won't fit in a car. 
do not	Gugy and Marzy don't drive very well. 

 **ar** says "ar" as in **star.**

star far 	jar car 
bar mar 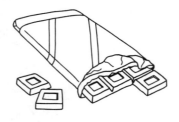	tar Marzy 
farmer scar 	garden charm

 **ing** says "ing" as in **ring.**

thing **ring**	string bring

wing sting	swing sing

king ding	stinger bring

Ing Words 97

Read the words. Then read the sentences below and circle the word that you think fits best in the blank.

ind says "ind" as in **find.**

find	mind
behind	rind
kind	bind

The sun is __________ a cloud.

wind
behind

I'll __________ a book.

find
kind

I think with my __________.

rind
mind

I'll __________ the clock.

behind
wind

ild says "ild" as in **child**.

wild   child   mild

The tiger is _____.

wild

child

Every person is a _____.

child

wild

Gugy likes _____ sauce.

child

mild

all says "all" as in **ball.**

hall	stall	fall
tall	wall	call

small  tall

Mom shops at the _____.

ball

mall

I'll _____ her on my phone.

hall

call

Don't _____ down the hill.

fall

wall

Look at the picture. Read the words. Circle the word that describes the picture.

OW says "OW" as in **crown.**
OU says "OU" as in **out.**

frown	cow	brown
down	how	clown

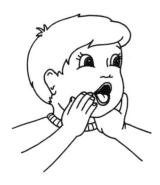	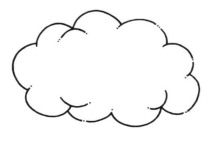	
shout	cloud	snout
clout	proud	loud

Ow - Ou Words

ed says "ed" as in **patted.**

painted dusted	
faded exploded	
cried hugged	
oozed sawed	
baked hopped	
walked raked	

  painted • hugged • hopped

exploded • sawed • walked

oy says "oy" as in **boy.**

oi says "oi" as in **boil.**

doy

boy

toy

joy

joyster

oyster

boil

toil

foil

coil

coin

toin

Sunday
Saturday
Friday
Thursday
Wednesday
Tuesday
Monday

ay says "ay" as in day.

say   stay   bay   May   away   day

Firemen _____,"Get _____ from the fire!"

say

away

jay

We sailed the boat in the _____.

bay

day

"Rain, rain, go _____
Come again another_____ ."

day

away

Flowers bloom in _____ .

play

May

ew says "ew" as in **mew.**

threw   new   few   blew

He _____ the ball into
the hoop.

tew

threw

The wind _____ the roof
off the house.

blew

dew

Dale got a _____
puppy for his birthday.

few

new

_____ may be on the grass
in the morning.

Few

Dew

Ew Words 105

aw says "aw" as in **paw**.
au says "au" as in **sauce**.

hawk

raw

paw

see-saw

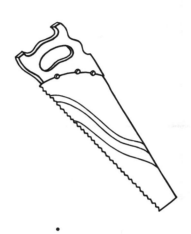

jaw

saw

haul

fault

taunt

haunt

fault

sauce

alt says "alt" as in **malt**.
alk says "alk" as in **walk**.

salt
halt

halt
waltz

malt
salt

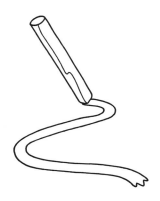

chalk
talk

talk
walk

walk
chalk

---

alt - alk Words **107**

ous says "ous" as in **gorgeous.**

gorgeous   famous

nervous   serious

cautious   joyous

Before a test, I'm _____.

joyous

nervous

Stealing is a _____ crime.

serious

gorgeous

He can <u>fl</u>ip and <u>fl</u>y.

Here is a dreadful dragon.

I can see a skinny skyscraper.

The string is striped.

Here is a <u>br</u>oom.

This is a <u>sp</u>oon.

This is a snap.

Here is a clown.

Here is a brush.

This is a block.

This is a spider.

Here is a swing.

Can a dog read a story?

yes   (no)

Will we ride on a cloud?

yes   no

Can we fly in a plane?

yes   no

Did Gugenheimer go to Mars?

yes   no

Will a baby drive a car?

yes   no

Can you find the clues in the words? Read the sentences.
Circle the correct answers.

COMPREHENSION
Discuss the logic of
the sentences.

Will we walk on a real star?

yes   no

Can owls and cats sail?

yes   no

Will a poodle turn on a light?

yes   no

Are the aged mice real?

yes   no

Can a bee sting?

yes   no

Can you find the clues in the words? Read the sentences.
Circle the correct answers.

Will the hawk haul the books?

yes   no

Miss Debby rides in a sleigh in the snow?

yes   no

Let's ride the merry-go-round?

yes   no

Bric and Brac stopped quickly?

yes   no

Can a cow fly?

yes   no

Can you find the clues in the words? Read the sentences. Circle the correct answers.

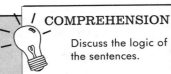

Is it dark at night?

yes   no

Can a bee sit on a flower?

yes   no

Will a ball dress in a skirt?

yes   no

Is Marzy from Mars?

yes   no

Does Cowgirl Cory ride at the ranch?

yes   no

Irregular Vowel Families Chart

Irregular Vowel Chant

I-G-H says **igh**, as in **sigh**
I-N-G says **ing**, as in **king**
I-N-D says **ind**, **behind**
I-L-D says **ild**, as in **child**
A-R says **ar**, as in **car**
O-R says **or**, this **or** that
O-I says **oi**, as in **oil**
O-Y says **oy**, as in **boy**
A-L-T says **alt**, as in **salt**
A-L-K says **alk**, as in **walk**
O-S-T says **ost**, as in **ghost**
O-L-D says **old**, as in **gold**
E-R says **er**, as in **jerk**
I-R says **ir**, as in **girl**
U-R says **ur**, as in **fur**
E-W says **ew**, as in **chew**
S-I-O-N **sion**, **explosion**
T-I-O-N **tion**, **attention**
E-I-G-H says **eigh**, as in **weigh**
A-L-L says **all**, as in **ball**
O-W says **ow**, as in **blow**
O-W says **ow**, as in **cow**
O-U says **ou**, as in **ouch**
A-Y says **ay**, hooray
O-U-S says **ous**, as in **gorgeous**
E-D says **ed**, patted
E-D says **t**, clapped
E-D says **d**, hugged
A-W says aw, paw
A-U says **au**, **caught**
O-O says o̅o̅, boo hoo
O-O says ŏŏ, as in **shook**

igh	ar
sigh	car
ing	**or**
king	this or that
ind	**oi**
behind	oil
ild	**oy**
child	boy

alt	er	sion
salt	jerk	explosion
alk	ir	tion
walk	girl	attention
ost	ur	eigh
ghost	fur	weigh
old	ew	all
gold	chew	ball

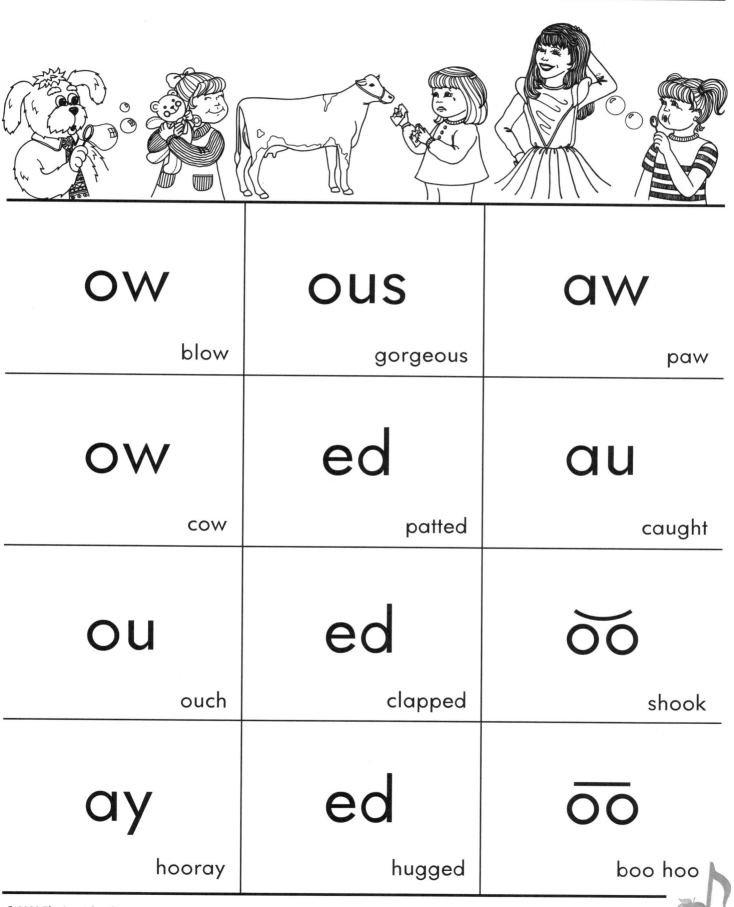

ow	**ous**	**aw**
blow	gorgeous	paw
ow	**ed**	**au**
cow	patted	caught
ou	**ed**	**o͝o**
ouch	clapped	shook
ay	**ed**	**o͞o**
hooray	hugged	boo hoo

Irregular Vowel Families Chart

Consonant Blends Chart

bl as in blow	**br** as in bread
cl as in clock	**cr** as in crown	**dr** as in dress
fl as in flag	**fr** as in frog	**gl** as in gloves
gr as in grapes	**pl** as in plum	**pr** as in princess 

sc as in scary	**sk** as in skates	**sl** as in sleep
scr as in scream	**sn** as in snake	**sp** as in spider
spr as in spring	**st** as in stick	**str** as in string
sw as in swing	**tr** as in trike	**tw** as in twins

Consonant Blends Chart

You have finished the last book in Challenger Phonics Fun!

Super!

Fantastic!

Hooray!

Yippee!

Great!

Wild!

Keep Reading! You will be a
star reader and speller!